PUZZLE MANIA

BRAIN TWISTERS

Puzzle Mania Brain Twisters
First published in 2007 by Budget Books Pty Ltd
45–55 Fairchild Street,
Heatherton VIC 3202 Australia

© Budget Books Pty Ltd 2007

2 4 6 8 10 9 7 5 3
08 10 12 11 09

ISBN 978 1 7418 1433 0

Printed and bound in India

Spot the Difference

Can you spot the ten differences between the two pictures?

1

Path Finder

See if you can trace a path through the smoke to lead the alien back to his crashed spaceship.

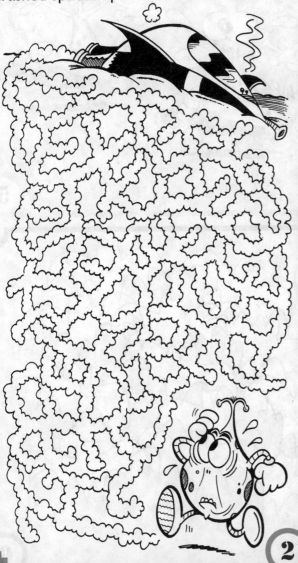

2

Hidden Language

Can you find all the names of different languages hidden in the following sentences?

1. If Ren chooses to come, it's OK.
2. You need anger management therapy.
3. Yes we dish up the food at 8.
4. Do you feel a tingle in your fingers?
5. The machine seems to have broken.
6. Your pet pig reeks.
7. Russ, I anticipate success.

3

PIECES OF EIGHT

All of the following words contain the letters OCT.
Can you fill in the missing letters, helped by the clues?

1. O C T ☐ ☐ ☐ ☐   Tenth month
2. ☐ O C T ☐ ☐   Medical adviser
3. ☐ O C T ☐ ☐ ☐ ☐   Coming out at night
4. O C T ☐ ☐ ☐   Eight-limbed sea creature
5. O C T ☐ ☐ ☐   Eight-sided shape

4

SPACE HOPPERS

Which strange hopping monster from outer space is the odd one out?

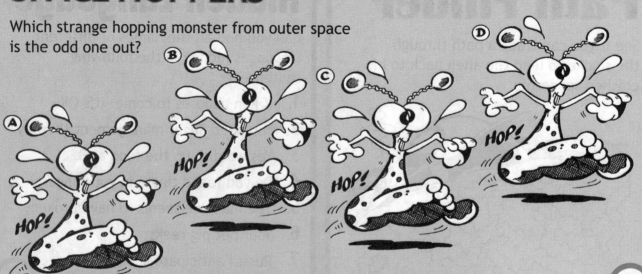

Bat Fan

5

6

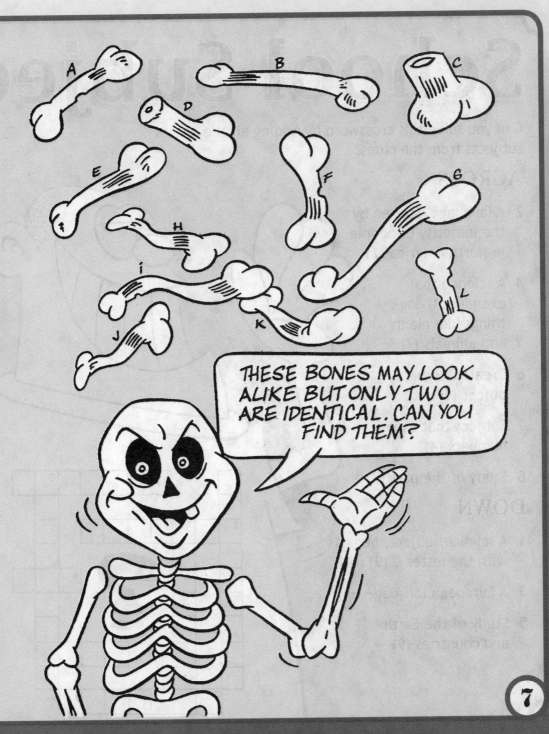

School Subject

Can you solve this crossword by finding all the school subjects from the clues?

ACROSS

2 A language, spoken by the majority of people in North America (7)

4 A science that examines living things like plants and animals (7)

6 Creative visual object (9)

7 Subject that uses numbers (4)

8 Study of the past (7)

DOWN

1 A science subject, begins with the letter C (9)

3 A European language (6)

5 Study of the Earth and countries (9)

What a Treat!

Can you discover where the six squares fit into the cartoon?

MAGIC SQUARE

Can you fill in the words of the square, helped by the clues? All the words read the same down as across.

1. Small baby's sleeping place

2. Travel on a vehicle

3. Produced by thinking

4. Part of a necklace

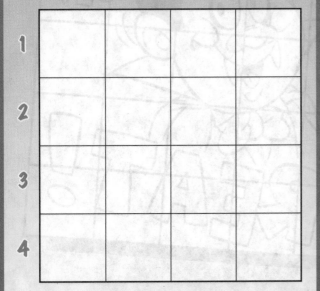

WHAT DOG?

Take the first letter of each object and write them on the dotted line. The letters spell out a breed of dog!

1	2	3	4	5	6	7	8	9

MONSTER MATCH

Which silhouette is the same as A?

SQUARE PAIR

Can you find the six pairs of identical squares?

Sudoku

Each row, column, and box must contain only one of each number from 1 to 9.

	5					2	1	
			3	5		6		
	3			9	7	4	8	
		9	2					
	2		7	4	5		6	
					8	5		
	1	8	4	6			5	
		5		7	1			
	7	6					9	

Cake Maker

It's birthday time again.
Can you work out:

1. Who is the oldest?

2. Who is the youngest?

3. How old is Lucy?

4. How old is Kelly?

5. Add Kelly's and Laura's ages.

6. Add Laura's and Zoe's ages.

7. Take Zoe's age from Kelly's.

8. Add all the ages together.

9. Add Zoe's and Lucy's.

FRANKIE'S FIND

Poor old Frankie Stein's ears have fallen off! Find a way through the maze to help him get them back.

Code Break

Code breaks are crosswords without clues. Every letter of the alphabet is used (you might find it useful to cross out the letters located by the grid as you find them) and each letter has its own number. For example, if number 12 turns out to be a "T," you can write in T wherever a square contains 12. When you have completed this puzzle, transfer the letters to the grid below to reveal a shredded veggie item.

	8		26	9	4	9	14	6	16		18	
1	21	4	4			20			1	9	20	11
	22		21	20	11	24	22	16	1		24	
	16		16			1		17		12		
18		6		10	24	8	24	12		12		3
						S	**I**	**T**				
19	22	9	20	16		12		22	18	25	9	14
19		22		14			16		16			9
16	24	3	7	12		13		14	16	16	1	8
22		18		8	5	21	24	1		1		7
	6		16			20			21		22	
	18		23	24	11	11	16	22	8		18	
20	9	15	16			16			16	9	8	12
	2		1	18	18	1	4	16	1		16	

A B C D E F G H I J K L M N O P Q R S T U V W X Y Z

1	2	3	4	5	6	7	8	9	10	11	12	13
							S				**T**	
14	15	16	17	18	19	20	21	22	23	24	25	26
										I		

Clue: Shredded veggie item

6	18	4	16	8	4	9	25

17

Ugly Mug

Which picture is different from the rest?

A

B

C

D

Continuous Capitals

Can you fill in the letters of the spiral puzzle, helped by the clues? The last letter of each word is the first letter of the next, and so on. The words need to be filled in clockwise.

1				2		
					6	
5			8			
			███			
7						
4						3

Capital of

1. France
2. Sweden
3. Spain
4. Ireland
5. Cyprus
6. The Netherlands
7. Russia
8. Poland

COMPUTERIZED

```
L P I H C O R C I M T O
X E I N T E R N E T R B
L A P T O P U R P C O Y
V V P L I A M E M I C R T
U I S C D T E M A I B E
X H D O U V M O U S E L
D C O P M P U T E
U T M E M O R Y Y
A O E X U I S
C S O N B T M
```

Find these eight words connected to computers.

☐ COMPUTER
☐ MEMORY
☐ MOUSE
☐ BYTE
☐ EMAIL
☐ LAPTOP
☐ INTERNET
☐ MICROCHIP

20

CROSSPIC

Use the pictures as clues to fill in the crossword. When complete, the circled sqares reading from left to right diagonally will reveal a hidden bird.

21

Tattooed

Color in the shapes with a dot to reveal what this man's tattoo is.

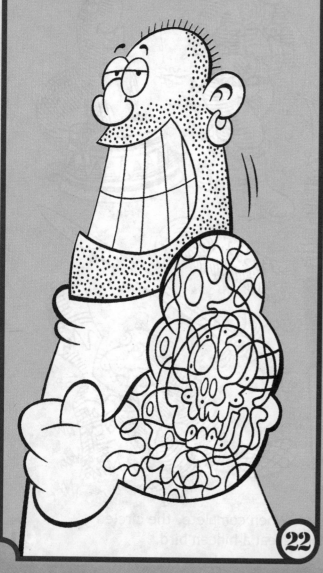

Place Setting

Rearrange the letters on the signpost to spell out four cold places.

1 NYOARW

2 IDCNEAL

3 GDRNEAELN

4 AALKAS

22

23

Sudoku

Each row, column, and box must contain only one of each number from 1 to 9.

				4		3	1	5
					8			7
		9		3	7			
5		6	8			7		
	1		9	6	5		4	
		8			3	5		6
			5	9		8		
7			3					
9	8	1		7				

Spot the Difference

CAT NAP

Help! My cat's stuck up the tree. Can you help me rescue him?

26

Dental Problem

Poor Colin has a toothache! Be brave and lead him to the dreaded dentist!

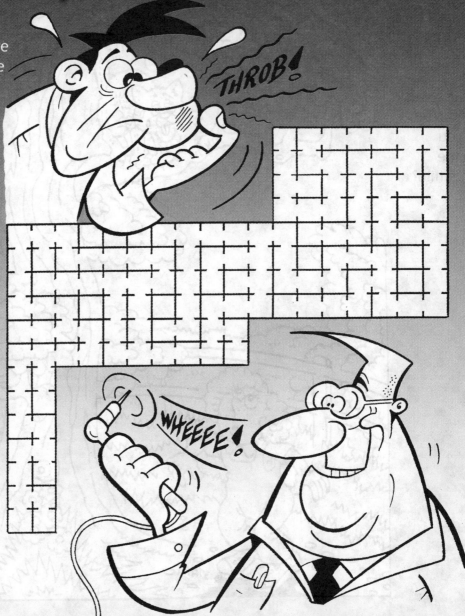

Lightning Strike

Use the grid references to find out where each of the squares belong in the picture.

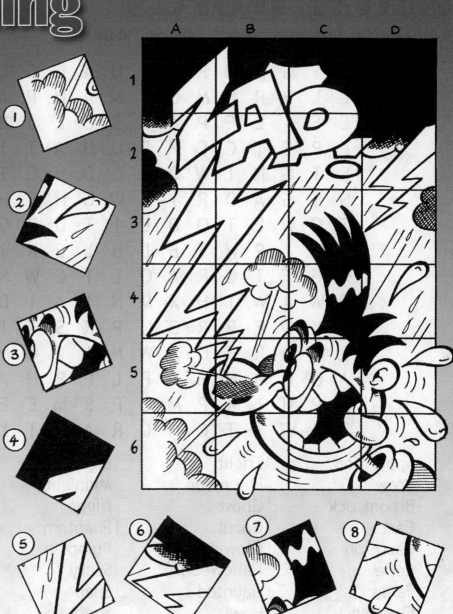

Witch Words

Witch words are hidden in the grid. Can you find them?

```
L Y G N O R D L U A C G C S F
L L V R E M O T N A H P A G T
E F I E E P A H S O E J B N A
P R E T C E P S U H A T I A E
S T G N I W O L G D H G T F R
N S G A D R I E W G H F H K T
E O N L T O D E I T U D G C R
E H I P H V E L B L E K I I O
W G T T G R A Q L T C W N T K
O W A W I H X M N I A I D S C
L K O E R R O U P R S T I M I
L O L R F O A W N I T C M O R
A O F B N H Y P L P R H A O T
H P N I K P M U P S M E E R C
Z S W I T C H C R A F T L B Y
```

- [ ] Apparition
- [ ] Brew
- [ ] Broomstick
- [ ] Cast
- [ ] Cauldron
- [ ] Eerie
- [ ] Fangs
- [ ] Floating
- [ ] Fly
- [ ] Fright
- [ ] Full moon
- [ ] Ghost
- [ ] Ghoul
- [ ] Glowing
- [ ] Halloween
- [ ] Haunted
- [ ] Howl
- [ ] Lantern
- [ ] Light
- [ ] Midnight
- [ ] Night
- [ ] Phantom
- [ ] Pumpkin
- [ ] Scary
- [ ] Shape
- [ ] Specter
- [ ] Spell
- [ ] Spirit
- [ ] Spook
- [ ] Trick or treat
- [ ] Vampire
- [ ] Weird
- [ ] Witch
- [ ] Witchcraft

29

Battle Line

Can you find the names of these famous battles in the bubblechain?

- Gettysburg
- Little Big Horn
- Iwo Jima
- Salamis
- Waterloo
- Hastings
- Culloden
- Somme

Sudoku

Each row, column, and box must contain only one of each number from 1 to 9.

		8	9			6	7	5
7					1	4		
		3			2			9
5				2				4
		1		3		8		
6				9				1
8			4			7		
		5	2					8
1	7	9			5	2		

Little Devils

Using face "A" as a guide, draw in the missing parts on the rest of the faces!

Ⓐ

Odd Alien

Can you find which alien is the odd one out?

32

33

SCARY

Unscramble the letters to form names of several scary things.

WHICH WITCH?

Which two pictures
of Winnie the witch
are the same?

TRIANGULAR

Fill in only the triangles and you will see a hidden picture.

CROSSWORD

ACROSS

5. Actor's part (4)
6. Cry aloud (4)
8. Conveyance for soldiers (9)
11. Containers for letters (9)
15. Type of earth (4)
16. Garment (4)

DOWN

1. Worry (4)
2. Singing voice (4)
3. Waist band (4)
4. Applaud (4)
7. Upset (5)
9. Move fast (3)
10. Frozen water (3)
11. Every (4)
12. Meat (4)
13. Rigid support (4)
14. Egyptian canal (4)

Sudoku

Each row, column, and box must contain only one of each number from 1 to 9.

5		7	8			4		3
			1	9	5			
					4			
9	3					8	5	
	7	5				3	6	
	1	8					9	7
			5					
			3	7	8			
4		3			2	9		5

39

OUT OF THIS WORLD

3 Letters
BIG
RAY
SKY

4 Letters
BEAM
FAST
LAND
LIFT
MOVE
SHIP
SPIN

5 Letters
ALIEN
CHASE
EERIE
FLASH
LARGE
NIGHT
SHAPE
SMALL
SOUND
TRACK
WORLD

6 Letters
ABDUCT
BEINGS
FOLLOW
OBJECT
PLANET

SAUCER
7 Letters
HUMMING
MACHINE
MYSTERY
STRANGE

8 Letters
CREATURE
FLASHING
GREEN MEN
HOVERING
WATCHING

9 Letters
ENCOUNTER

HUMMING

40

CHEESE PLEASE!

Rearrange the jumbled letters below, to spell out five names of cheeses!

1. DAME
2. RIBE
3. HEADRDC
4. TILTSON
5. ARMENAPS

Memorize

How good a witness would you be? Look at this picture for 20 seconds, then cover the picture and answer the questions below.

1. Can a fish be seen in the water?
2. Is the man wearing a wrist-watch?
3. Is the man wearing black pants?
4. Are there any flowers in the grass?
5. Can a house be seen in the distance?

View Finder Please!

Fill in the grid by solving the clues, then find an answer to the clue by arranging the shaded squares.

Clue: Sport

ACROSS
1. Fundamental
4. Egg-shapes
6. Queue of traffic
7. Night before
8. Sharp
9. Beers
10. Fix

DOWN
1. Drill a hole
2. Direction finder
3. Habit
5. Alter
6. Wobbly food

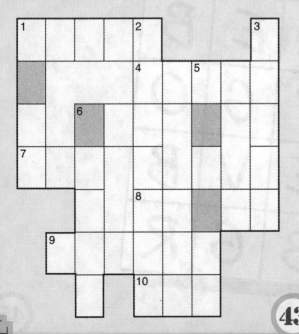

PENCIL BOX

Can you find the items usually found in your school pencil case hidden in the following sentences?

1. Peru, Leroy, is in South America.
2. Open Cilla's briefcase.
3. The eclipse will happen soon.
4. I stopped her as Eric ran past.
5. Ben's harp energized the school orchestra.
6. Telecom passes on savings to their customers.

School Daze

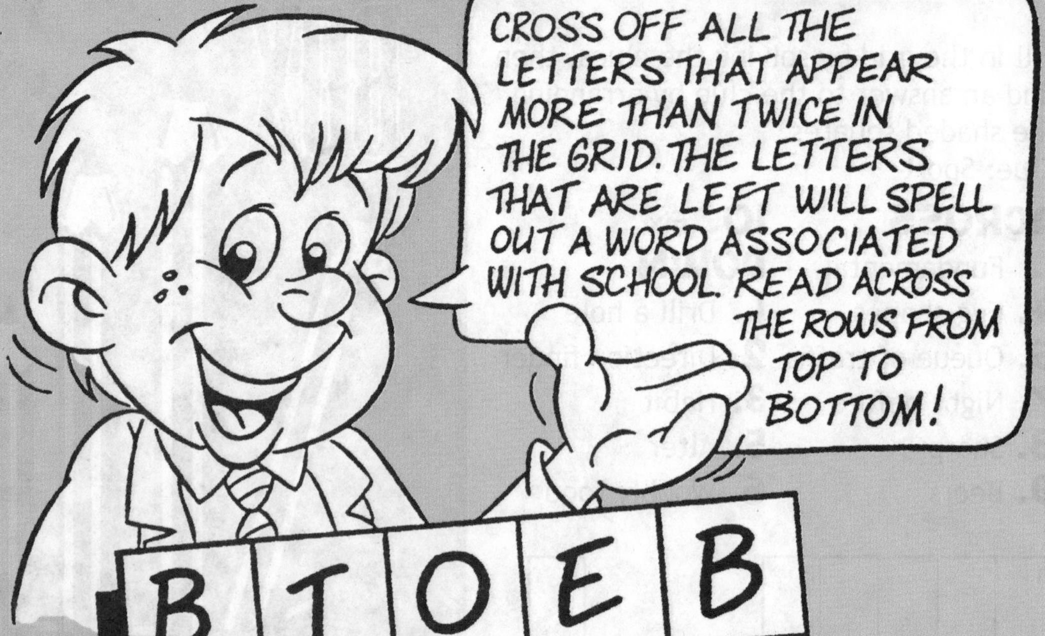

B	T	O	E	B
A	O	V	G	O
C	H	E	V	B
G	V	B	G	R

Messy Nessie

The picture of Nessie at the top left of the page is complete.

Circle what is missing from the remaining seven pictures.

TRICK OR TREAT

Look at this picture for one minute, then cover the page and see if you can remember all the items that are in the monster's cloak!

Sudoku

Each row, column, and box must contain only one of each number from 1 to 9.

	5	1					3	
9			1	3	8		4	
		6			7		1	
							9	7
		3	4		5	2		
2	8							
	9		5			4		
	4		2	1	3			8
	6					1	7	

Spot the Difference

Can you spot the
ten differences
between the
two pictures?

CAST A SPELL

Rearrange the letters below to spell out the name of a Halloween monster!

F N A R I A R E T N K T S E N

Little Monster

Which square is from the picture?

(A)

(B)

(C)

51

DOG LEADS

Find each word of the riddle in the block of letters. (The words may read up or down, from left to right, from right to left, or diagonally.) Then draw a ring around each word. Finally, copy the leftover letters – the ones you haven't drawn a ring around – in order and you will have the answer to the riddle.

A	K	B	E	S	T
D	W	E	D	O	G
N	T	H	E	F	A
I	T	C	H	P	D
K	T	A	H	W	S
T	I	M	E	O	G

WHAT KIND OF DOG KEEPS THE BEST TIME?

52

Change a Letter

Add a letter to each of the words on the left to make a new word, helped by the clues. If you collect all the added letters together you will find the sweet-smelling promise of fall fruit.

word		clue
set		somewhere to sit
send		use money
rum		rear of an animal
seep		get some rest
bad		part of a necklace
tale		you sit at it to eat
cap		applaud
son		in a short while
top		Halt!
jet		joke
fund		discovered
sack		hit

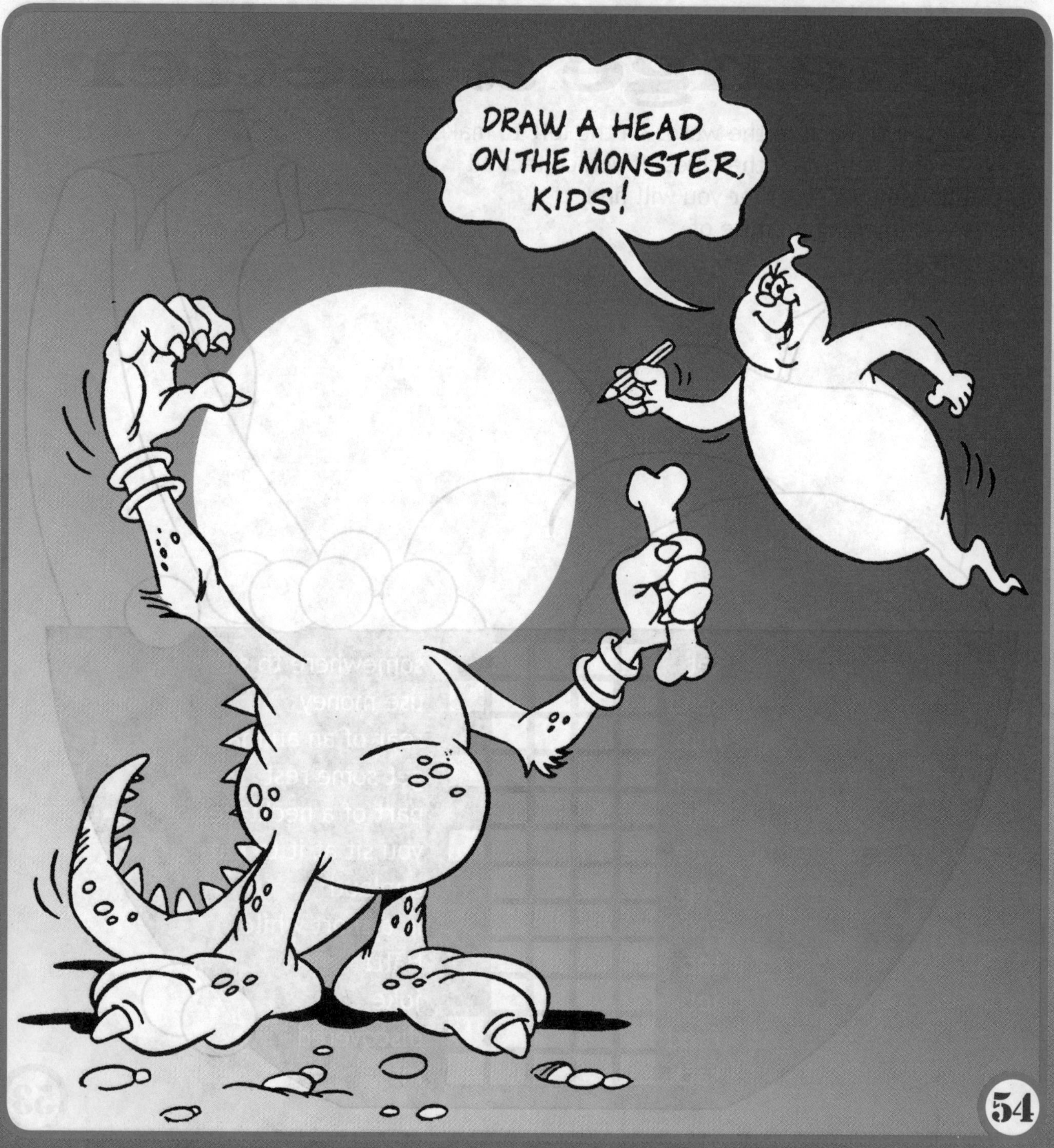
DRAW A HEAD ON THE MONSTER, KIDS!

HOLIDAY HAIR-DO

Can you find the answers
to the holiday destinations?

ACROSS

1. Island "Down Under"

4. The party capital of Brazil
   famous for its carnival

6. Southern state of the USA
   – Miami is in it

7. Italian capital

9. Central European country
   famous for its mountains and skiing

DOWN

1. Capital of Greece

2. A Canary Island

3. Southern European Country

5. Island country to the west of England

8. French site of the Eiffel Tower

10. Japan's largest city

55

Which two creatures are identical?

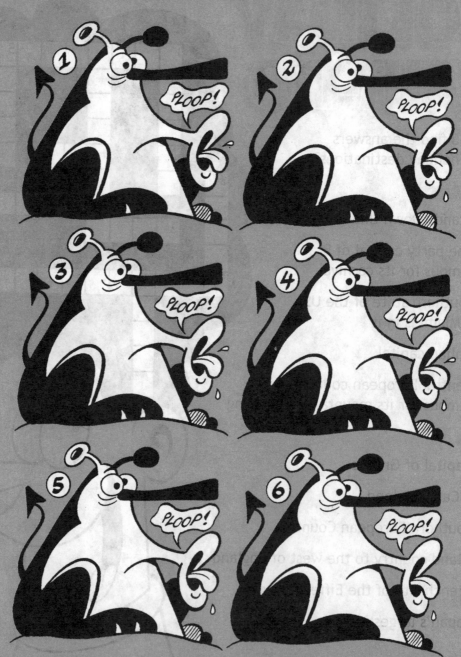

CROSSPIC

Using the pictures as clues, fill in the grid and discover a game hidden in the circled squares.

57

LET'S FACE IT

ENERGIZE ERRORS

Can you spot the ten differences?

Sudoku

Each row, column, and box must contain only one of each number from 1 to 9.

	1	5			3	8		
		3	5				4	
6					2			7
	4			6		7		
2		8		4		5		3
		6		3			9	
9			3					2
	8				9	6		
		1	6			4	7	

61

MIXED PICK

These pictures have gotten mixed up. Which order should they appear in?

A

B

C

D

E

F

Bird Box

Fill in the names of birds in the puzzle below. If you do so correctly you will find an item of food that gives you good health.

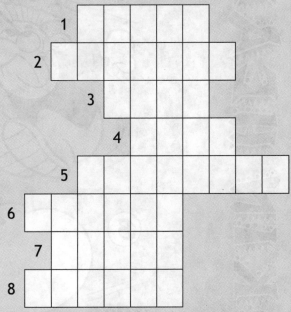

1. Red breasted bird
2. Small bird with grey brown feathers
3. Black bird whose name sounds like a chess piece
4. Black bird whose name sounds like a cockerel's cry
5. Exotic bird with vertical plumage on its head
6. Bird often called "Polly"
7. High soaring hook-beaked bird
8. Black and white destructive bird

Spot the Difference

Can you spot the ten differences between the two pictures?

OBJECTIVE

FOUL PLAY

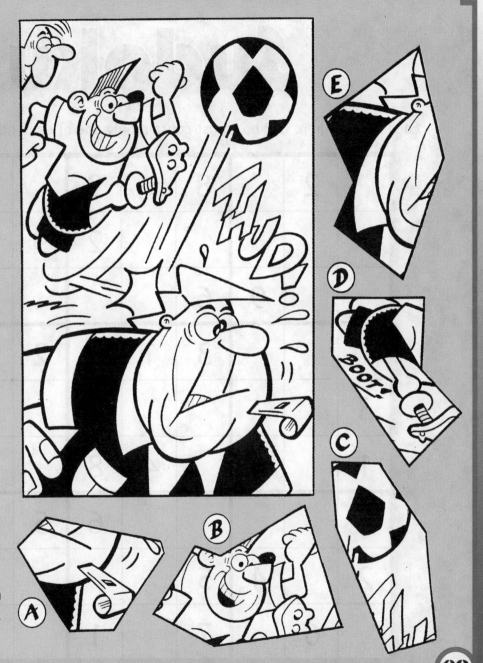

Robbie has mis-kicked his pass and hit the Ref. Can you find which two pieces are not part of the picture?

Sudoku

Each row, column, and box must contain only one of each number from 1 to 9.

	2		8		9		7	
					2	9		4
		9	6					
7			3	1		2		6
3								1
1		6		4	8			9
					6	5		
2		4	5					
	6		7		1		2	

TUNE IN

Find the instruments hidden in the grid.

```
C X O H A R M O N I C A S
H A U J D R P M S H T T A
I J B R N C R L B V A R X
M P U U H A L B O M K R O
E M J Q T E B A B S P N P
S M T I B R F O R S O Y H
E Y U G O P U I H I K V O
P G K V J R V M D P N D N
I S U H I U G R P D R E E
P M L N G O O A S E L U T
G T E S L C L M N G T E U
A R L B C K P I A N O K L
B S E A K U P H N I N T F
```

ACCORDION   FIDDLE   SAXOPHONE

BAGPIPES   FLUTE   TAMBOURINE

BANJO   GUITAR   TRUMPET

BELLS   HARMONICA   TUBA

CHIMES   HARP   UKULELE

CLARINET   ORGAN   VIOLIN

DRUMS   PIANO

Crossword

ACROSS

3. Large sea creature (5)
5. Big (5)
6. Animal (5)
8. Bulls, cows, etc. (6)
12. Season (6)
15. Not sharp (5)
16. Set of bells (5)
17. Contest (5)

DOWN

1. Color (5)
2. Legal document (4)
3. Watering place (4)
4. Hobble (4)
7. Thin (4)
9. Urban community (4)
10. Gluttony (5)
11. Excuse (4)
13. Irritate (4)
14. Work hard (4)

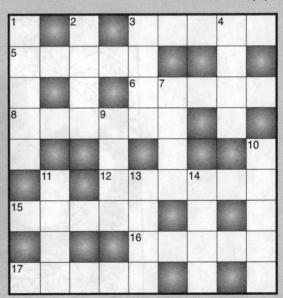

ALL CHANGE

CAN YOU SPOT TEN DIFFERENCES?

Just a Bite

Which shape matches the bite that Clive the Caterpillar has taken out of the leaf?

73

Sweet Treat

In which order do you pick up the candy canes, so you don't disturb the rest?

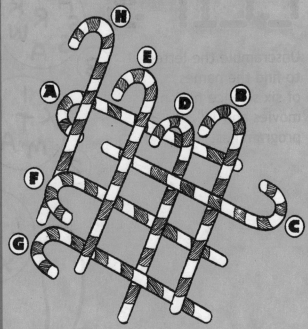

74

FILM CLIPS

Unscramble the letters to find the names of six science fiction movies and TV programmes.

WINTER WORDS

See if you can find all the words to the right of the page in the wordsearch. The words can go up, down, diagonally, forward, and even backwards!

SLEDGE
MITTENS
HAT
SCARF
SNOWMAN
WINTER
SNOW
ICE
COLD
GLOVES
BOOTS

```
G L O V E S A H
N O R E T N I W
A W S B W O N S
M I T T E N S L
W C O A V C U E
O O O H A R P D
N L B R G T O G
S D F M F I C E
```

SMASHING TIME

Which shape is the same as the broken window?

Spot the Difference

Can you spot the ten differences between the two pictures?

78

Snow Way!

Which two snowflakes are different from the rest?

① ② ③ ④
⑤ ⑥
⑦ ⑧ ⑨

Tiger, Tiger

Cross out all the letters that appear more than once and find out Tiger Woods' real christian name.

A J H M O F
K E B P L Q
G N D G N R
F O Q I S T
K B U A T C
J S U P H M

Santa's Route

Help Santa through the maze to find his reindeer.

COUNTRY WIDE

Can you find the names of these countries in the wordsearch? The letters that are left spell out the country where I'm from.

E	C	N	A	R	F	N	E
E	C	A	N	A	D	A	W
N	E	R	I	E	S	A	Y
G	U	S	A	P	I	W	N
L	Z	E	A	R	L	A	A
A	A	I	T	A	N	L	M
N	N	S	U	K	D	E	R
D	U	P	E	R	U	S	E
A	O	C	I	X	E	M	G

ENGLAND

UK

WALES

USA

PERU

CANADA

GERMANY

FRANCE

AUSTRIA

MEXICO

EIRE

SPAIN

82

Lunch Time

How many food names can you find spelled around this boy?

Carol Stinger

Fill in the blank spaces on the right to reveal the carol, then rearrange the letters you've added to make a word associated with Santa Claus!

In your Face

Can you find all the parts of the face and head hidden in the following sentences?

1. I'm out here!

2. This lychee keeps rolling off the table.

3. Which individual is responsible for this?

4. I find pianos extremely boring.

5. We are leaving now.

6. Before heading abroad, check your passport.

7. Salvador Dali produced strange paintings.

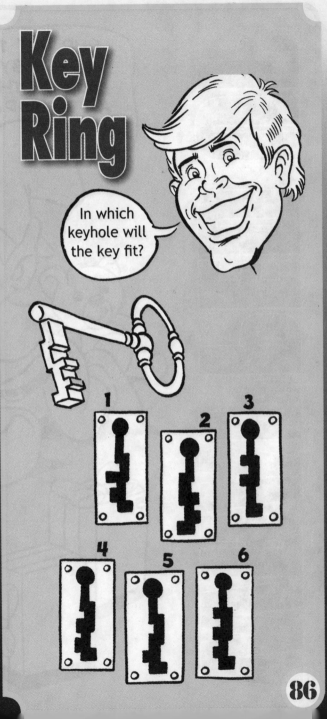

Key Ring

In which keyhole will the key fit?

FIND OUT THE NAME OF SANTA'S HELPER BY WORKING OUT THE CODE ON THE PRESENTS.
A=1 B=2 AND C=3.

87

Sudoku

Each row, column, and box must contain only one of each number from 1 to 9.

	8			9		5		
			4	3			9	
		7		2				6
	5	4		1			8	
3	6						2	7
	1			7		6	4	
9				5		7		
	7			6	9			
		2		4			5	

POST CODE

See if you can work out this letter sent in code to Santa Claus. The words are spelled in reverse and read from the bottom to the top, right to left.

REHPYC YENDIS
YLURT SRUOY
TUO KROW
OT DRAH ERA TAHT
SRETTEL GNITIRW
EKIL I ESUACEB
RAEY SIHT TNESERP
A ROF KOOB EDOC
S'YPS A EKIL DLUOW I
ATNAS RAED

Star Filling

Fit the ten names into the grid, so the center column reveals the surname of one of the names across. (Grand Prix driver.)

BARRY   JIM   PAUL

GRAHAM   LEO   PERCIVAL

JACK   MICHAEL

JASON   NATHANIEL

Which girl is different from the rest?

1

2

3

4

Sudoku

Each row, column, and box must contain only one of each number from 1 to 9.

3		6		9		2		1
		8				9	4	
					4			5
	5		4					
9		3	8		2	1		4
					1		9	
7			1					
	2	9				8		
1		4		2		6		7

Present Suprise

See if you can find the following Christmas presents in the wordsearch.

COMPACT DISC

VIDEO TAPE

SHOES

SHIRT

JACKET

DOLL

PEN

SWEETS

PERFUME

FOOTBALL

C	O	L	E	M	U	F	R	E	P	O
J	O	T	L	O	I	V	E	O	D	L
A	B	M	U	N	E	I	V	A	C	L
C	L	O	P	U	G	D	R	O	F	O
K	A	H	N	A	S	E	C	O	Y	D
E	B	E	T	I	C	O	O	F	T	G
T	P	R	G	S	O	T	R	I	R	E
C	O	V	E	W	B	A	D	Y	I	L
H	I	O	N	A	S	P	R	I	H	O
U	H	E	L	L	U	E	B	A	S	I
S	A	L	S	T	E	E	W	S	E	C

93

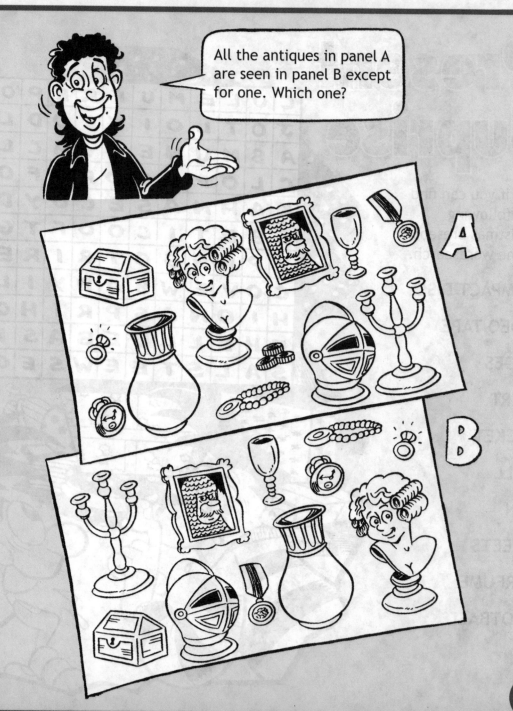

Pete's Portable

Which remote control button switches on Pete's portable TV?

JOIN THE DOTS

Starting at no. 1, take your pencil and connect all the dots to make a secret picture.

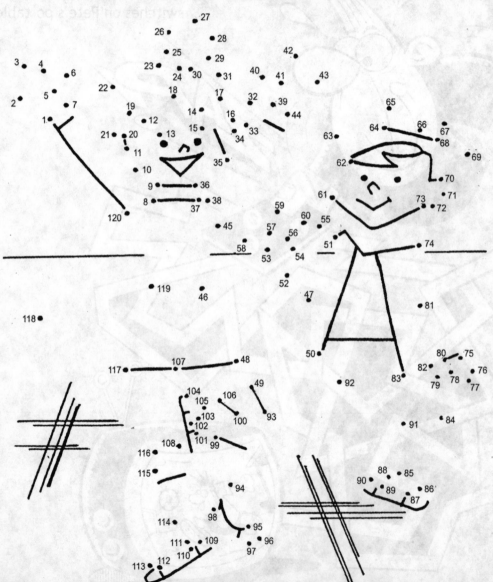

Super Hero Hitch

Can you spot ten differences between the two pictures?

Acrostic

Solve the clues and enter the answers in Grid A. If your answers are correct you will find, reading down the first column, the name of an author. Transfer the numbered letters to Grid B to reveal the title of one of his stories.

1. Bright and merry
2. Large basket of food
3. Type of calendar
4. Praying beads
5. Giving generously
6. Anticipate
7. Enjoy the taste of food
8. Long for
9. Ask to the party
10. Traveling show
11. Edible part of a nut
12. Overjoyed
13. Chewy candy
14. A toboggan

6		5	1	4	8	7	3	2	6	7		5	6	4	10	9

FRIENDS

Can you find all the names of the characters in *Friends* and the places they spend their time hidden in the wordsearch?

- [ ] APARTMENT
- [ ] CENTRAL PERK
- [ ] CHANDLER
- [ ] JOEY
- [ ] MONICA
- [ ] MUSEUM
- [ ] OFFICE
- [ ] PHOEBE
- [ ] RACHEL
- [ ] RESTAURANT
- [ ] ROSS
- [ ] STORE
- [ ] THEATER

```
C P E R L S R A I N R
H E H D S U S L O T E
A L N O A L T M A H S
N A R T E C O I P E T
D C E H R B R Y A A A
L A C H O A E R R T U
E A R S C O L Y T E R
R O I I J P H P M R A
J R N R A H E J E Y N
P O O F F I C E N R T
M U S E U M M O T O K
```

CAT FLAP

DROOL!

Starting with one of the top letters and finishing at the question mark, can you find the name of something that the cat is thinking of?

TRIANGULAR

Fill in only the triangles and you will see a hidden picture.

Sudoku

Each row, column, and box must contain only one of each number from 1 to 9.

7	8				5		3	4
						5	7	
			3			9	2	
5	1	9			7			
6								9
			4			1	5	2
	5	2				1		
	4	6						
1	7		9				6	5

Solutions

Puzzle 1

Puzzle 2

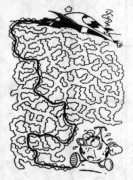

Puzzle 3

1. French (IF REN CHooses)
2. German (anGER MANagement)
3. Swedish (YeS WE DISH)
4. Latin (feeL A TINgle)
5. Chinese (maCHINE SEems)
6. Greek (piG REEKs)
7. Russian (RUSS, I ANticipate)

Puzzle 4

1. October, 2. Doctor, 3. Nocturnal, 4. Octopus, 5. Octagon.

Puzzle 5

Monster C – spot missing near little toe.

Puzzle 6

12 bats

Puzzle 7

H and J are the same.

Puzzle 8

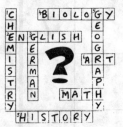

Puzzle 9

Puzzle 10

1. Crib, 2. Ride, 3. Idea, 4. Bead.

Puzzle 11

1. Door, 2. Arm, 3. Leaf, 4. Monster, 5. Ankle, 6. Three, 7. Ink, 8. Ace, 9. Nail. – Dalmatian

Puzzle 12

Silhouette D.

Puzzle 13

A4-D6, C4-D8, B1-C7, C2-B7, A5-A8, D1-C3

Puzzle 14

9	5	7	6	8	4	2	1	3
1	8	4	3	5	2	6	7	9
6	3	2	1	9	7	4	8	5
5	4	9	2	1	6	8	3	7
8	2	3	7	4	5	9	6	1
7	6	1	9	3	8	5	2	4
3	1	8	4	6	9	7	5	2
2	9	5	8	7	1	3	4	6
4	7	6	5	2	3	1	9	8

Puzzle 15

1. Lucy, 2. Zoe, 3. 14, 4. 12, 5. 24, 6. 23, 7. 1, 8. 49, 9. 25.

Solutions

Puzzle 16

Puzzle 17

S		B	A	L	A	N	C	E		O	
D	U	L	L			M			D	A	M	P
R			U	M	P	I	R	E	D		I	T
E		E		D		Y		T		G
O		C		V	I	S	I	T	T		G
F	R	A	M	E		T		R	O	W	A	N
F		R		N			E		E		A
E	I	G	H	T		J		N	E	E	D	S
R		O		S	Q	U	I	D		D	H
	C		E			M			U	R
	O		K	I	P	P	E	R	S		O
M	A	Z	E			E			E	A	S	T
X		D	O	O	D	L	E	D		E

Shredded veggie item:
Coleslaw

Puzzle 18

Picture D.

Puzzle 19

1. Paris, 2. Stockholm,
3. Madrid, 4. Dublin,
5. Nicosia, 6. Amsterdam,
7. Moscow, 8. Warsaw.

Puzzle 20

L	P	I	H	C	O	R	C	I	M	T	O
X	E	I	N	T	E	R	N	E	T	R	B
L	A	P	T	O	P	U	R	P	C	O	Y
V	P	L	I	A	M	E	M	I	C	R	T
U	I	S	C	D	T	E	M	A	I	B	E
X	H	D	O	U	V	M	O	U	S	E	L
D	C	O	P	M	P	U	T	E
U	T	M	E	M	O	R	Y
A	O	E	X	U	I	S
C	S	O	N	B	T	M

Puzzle 21

S	E	A	L
S	W	O	R	D
B	E	A	V	E	R
G	A	L	L	E	O	N
	B	U	G	L	E	R
		P	I	L	O	T
			C	L	A	W

Puzzle 22

Puzzle 23

1. Norway, 2. Iceland,
3. Greenland, 4. Alaska.

Puzzle 24

8	7	2	6	4	9	3	1	5
1	3	4	2	5	8	9	6	7
6	5	9	1	3	7	4	8	2
5	9	6	8	2	4	7	3	1
3	1	7	9	6	5	2	4	8
4	2	8	7	1	3	5	9	6
2	6	3	5	9	1	8	7	4
7	4	5	3	8	6	1	2	9
9	8	1	4	7	2	6	5	3

Puzzle 25

AAGHHH!

Puzzle 26

Puzzle 27

Solutions

Puzzle 28

1. A-6, 2. D-4, 3. C-5, 4. A-1, 5. A-4, 6. D-2, 7. C-4, 8. B-6.

Puzzle 29

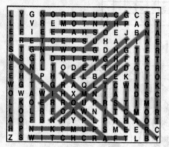

Puzzle 30

Puzzle 31

2	1	8	9	4	3	6	7	5
7	9	6	8	5	1	4	3	2
4	5	3	6	7	2	1	8	9
5	8	7	1	2	6	3	9	4
9	2	1	5	3	4	8	6	7
6	3	4	7	9	8	5	2	1
8	6	2	4	1	9	7	5	3
3	4	5	2	6	7	9	1	8
1	7	9	3	8	5	2	4	6

Puzzle 33

Alien A

Puzzle 34

Ghost, Vampire, Ghoul, Werewolf, Witch, Zombie.

Puzzle 35

Rye, Wheat, Barley, Carrots, Oats, Potatoes.

Puzzle 36

C and F

Puzzle 37

PUZZLE 38

Across: 5. Role, 6. Call, 8. Troopship, 11. Envelopes, 15. Clay, 16. Robe.
Down: 1. Fret, 2. Alto, 3. Sash, 4. Clap, 7. Spill, 9. Run, 10. Ice, 11. Each, 12. Veal, 13. Prop, 14. Suez.

Puzzle 39

5	9	7	8	2	6	4	1	3
3	4	2	1	9	5	7	8	6
8	6	1	7	3	4	5	2	9
9	3	4	2	6	7	8	5	1
2	7	5	9	8	1	3	6	4
6	1	8	4	5	3	2	9	7
7	2	6	5	4	9	1	3	8
1	5	9	3	7	8	6	4	2
4	8	3	6	1	2	9	7	5

Puzzle 40

C	R	E	A	T	U	R	E			C						
	N							W		H		F	L	A	S	H
M	A	C	H	I	N	E		A		A		L				O
Y	O			E		T		S	H	A	P	E				V
S	O	U	N	D		R		C		E		S				E
T	N		N	I	G	H	T		S	H	I	P				R
E	T	S	E			I		I		I						
R	E	K		N		A	N	S		N						
Y	R	A	Y	F	G		B	I	G		P	G				
	L		A			D		L			I					
	B	E	I	N	G	S		H	U	M	M	I	N	G		O
	E		T			C										B
P	L	A	N	E	T		L	I	F	T				S		J
A			A			A	O			S	T	R	A	N	G	E
G	R	E	E	N	M	E	N		L		M			U		C
G			O			D			L		A			C		T
B	E	A	M		V			W	O	R	L	D		E		
			E						W			L		T	R	A	C	K

Puzzle 41

1. Edam, 2. Brie, 3. Cheddar, 4. Stilton, 5. Parmesan.

Puzzle 43

B	A	S	I	C			U	
O			O	V	A	L	S	
R		J	A	M		D	A	
E	V	E		P		J	G	
		L		A	C	U	T	E
A	L	E	S	S				
		Y		S	E	T		

Sport: Judo.

Solutions

Puzzle 44

1. Ruler (PeRU, LERoy)
2. Pencil (OPEN CiLla's)
3. Pens (hapPEN Soon)
4. Eraser (hER AS ERic)
5. Sharpener (Ben'S HARP ENERgized)
6. Compass (TeleCOM PASSes)

Puzzle 45

Teacher.

Puzzle 46

Puzzle 48

8	5	1	6	2	4	7	3	9
9	2	7	1	3	8	5	4	6
4	3	6	9	5	7	8	1	2
5	1	4	3	8	2	6	9	7
6	7	3	4	9	5	2	8	1
2	8	9	7	6	1	3	5	4
1	9	8	5	7	6	4	2	3
7	4	5	2	1	3	9	6	8
3	6	2	8	4	9	1	7	5

Puzzle 49

Puzzle 50

Frankenstein.

Puzzle 51

Square B

Puzzle 52

A watch dog

Puzzle 53

seat, spend, rump, sleep, bead, table, clap, soon, stop, jest, found, smack.
– Apple blossom.

Puzzle 55

Puzzle 56

3 and 4

Puzzle 57

Puzzle 58

Lisa

Puzzle 59

Ghost

Puzzle 60

Solutions

Puzzle 61

7	1	5	4	9	3	8	2	6
8	2	3	5	7	6	9	4	1
6	9	4	1	8	2	3	5	7
3	4	9	2	6	5	7	1	8
2	7	8	9	4	1	5	6	3
1	5	6	8	3	7	2	9	4
9	6	7	3	5	4	1	8	2
4	8	2	7	1	9	6	3	5
5	3	1	6	2	8	4	7	9

Puzzle 62

13 bones

Puzzle 63

1. F, 2. C, 3. E, 4. D, 5. A, 6. B.

Puzzle 64

1. Robin, 2. Sparrow, 3. Rook, 4. Crow, 5. Cockatoo, 6. Parrot, 7. Eagle, 8. Magpie.

Puzzle 65

Silhouette A

Puzzle 66

Puzzle 67

Earring, Handbag, Lipstick, Hairbrush, Carkeys, Eyeshadow.

Puzzle 68

B and D

Puzzle 69

4	2	1	8	3	9	6	7	5
6	3	7	1	5	2	9	8	4
5	8	9	6	7	4	3	1	2
7	9	8	3	1	5	2	4	6
3	4	2	9	6	7	8	5	1
1	5	6	2	4	8	7	3	9
8	1	3	4	2	6	5	9	7
2	7	4	5	9	3	1	6	8
9	6	5	7	8	1	4	2	3

Puzzle 70

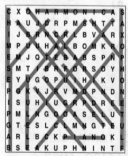

Puzzle 71

Across: Whale, 4. Large, 6. Llama, 8. Cattle, 12. Winter, 15. Blunt, 16. Chime, 17. Match.

Down: 1. Black, 2. Writ, 3. Well, 4. Limp, 7. Lean, 9. Town, 10. Greed, 11. Plea, 13. Itch, 14. Toil.

Puzzle 72

Puzzle 73

Shape C

Puzzle 74

E, C, B, G, D, F, H, A.

Puzzle 75

1. *X Files*, 2. *Matrix*, 3. *Star Wars*, 4. *Doctor Who*, 5. *Red Dwarf*, 6. *Star Trek*.

Puzzle 76

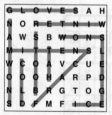

Solutions

Puzzle 77
Piece B.

Puzzle 78

Puzzle 79
3 and 7.

Puzzle 80
Eldric.

Puzzle 81

Puzzle 82

New Zealand

Puzzle 83 Turkey, Yogurt, Trifle, Lemonade, Eggs, Sausage, Sage, Onion, Nuts, Stuffing, Ginger, Raisins, Salami, Icing, Ham, Mint.

Puzzle 84 Silent Night, Holy Night. The word is SLEIGH.

Puzzle 85

1. Mouth (I'M OUT Here).
2. Cheek (lyCHEE Keeps).
3. Chin (whiCH Individual).
4. Nose (piaNOS Extremely).
5. Ear (WE ARe).
6. Forehead (BeFORE HEADing).
7. Lip (DaLI Produced).

Puzzle 86
No. 4

Puzzle 87

Puzzle 88

4	8	3	1	9	6	5	7	2
5	2	6	4	3	7	8	9	1
1	9	7	8	2	5	4	3	6
7	5	4	6	1	2	3	8	9
3	6	9	5	8	4	1	2	7
2	1	8	9	7	3	6	4	5
9	4	1	2	5	8	7	6	3
8	7	5	3	6	9	2	1	4
6	3	2	7	4	1	9	5	8

Puzzle 89

Dear Santa,

I would like a spy's code book for a present this year because I like writing letters that are hard to work out.

Yours truly, Sidney Cypher.

Puzzle 90 In order

JASON
JACK
NATHANIEL
PAUL
JIM
MICHAEL
PERCIVAL
GRAHAM
LEO
BARRY
Michael Schumacher.

Solutions

Puzzle 91
No. 1 is different – the eyelash on right eye is missing.

Puzzle 92

3	4	6	5	9	8	2	7	1
5	1	8	2	3	7	9	4	6
2	9	7	6	1	4	3	8	5
8	5	1	4	6	9	7	3	2
9	7	3	8	5	2	1	6	4
4	6	2	3	7	1	5	9	8
7	3	5	1	8	6	4	2	9
6	2	9	7	4	5	8	1	3
1	8	4	9	2	3	6	5	7

Puzzle 93

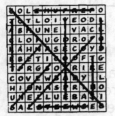

Puzzle 94
Coins.

Puzzle 95
Button 2.

Puzzle 96

Puzzle 97

Puzzle 98

C	H	E	E	R	Y
H	A	M	P	E	R
A	D	V	E	N	T
R	O	S	A	R	Y
L	A	V	I	S	H
E	X	P	E	C	T
S	A	V	O	U	R
D	E	S	I	R	E
I	N	V	I	T	E
C	I	R	C	U	S
K	E	R	N	E	L
E	L	A	T	E	D
N	O	U	G	A	T
S	L	E	D	G	E

A Christmas Carol – Charles Dickens

Puzzle 99

Puzzle 100
1. Guitar, 2. Drums, 3. Violin, 4. Clarinet, 5. Keyboards, 6. Cello.

Puzzle 101
Salmon

Puzzle 102

Puzzle 103

7	8	1	2	9	5	6	3	4
2	9	3	1	4	6	5	7	8
4	6	5	3	7	8	9	2	1
5	1	9	8	2	7	3	4	6
6	2	4	5	1	3	7	8	9
8	3	7	4	6	9	1	5	2
3	5	2	6	8	1	4	9	7
9	4	6	7	5	2	8	1	3
1	7	8	9	3	4	2	6	5